KELP FORESTS

SCOTLAND'S LIVING LANDSCAPES

KELP FORESTS

SCOTLAND'S LIVING LANDSCAPES

by

Ian Fuller

SCOTTISH NATURAL HERITAGE

SNH Publications, Battleby, Redgorton, Perth, Scotland

First published in 1999 by Scottish Natural Heritage,
Battleby, Redgorton, Perth PH1 3EW
Tel: 01738 627921 Fax: 01738 827411
E-mail:pubs@redgore.demon.co.uk
Web site: http://www.snh.org.uk

Series Editor: John Baxter
Editor: Claire Green (SNH)
Designer: Pam Malcolm (SNH)
Designed and produced by SNH Publications
Printed in Scotland by Nevisprint, Fort William

Photographs: Aberdeen University Library 25 bottom, **John Baxter/SNH** 2 bottom, 6, 23, 25 top, **Laurie Campbell** 1, 2 top, 21 top & bottom, **David Connor/JNCC** cover top left, 15,16, **Rohan Holt/JNCC** 7 bottom, 10, 12 right, 13 bottom left & right, 17 left, 18, 20 bottom right, **Paul Kay** inside front, 4, 14 top, 27 top, **Elinor Murray/JNCC** 17 bottom right, **Bill Sanderson/JNCC** 24, **Sue Scott** cover right, bottom left & centre, v, vi, viii, 3 top, 5 left & right, 7 top, 11, 12 left, 13 top left & top right, 14 bottom, 17 top right, 19 top left, top right & bottom, 20 bottom left, 22, 27 bottom, 28.

Illustrations: Claire Hewitt

Cover photographs (clockwise from top left): 1. Kelp stipes holdfast encrusted with life;
2. Kelp forest; 3. Jewel anemone; 4. Top shell.

ISBN 1 85397 014 X paperback
A CIP record is held at the British Library
NP3K0904R1

Contents

Sea urchins grazing kelp

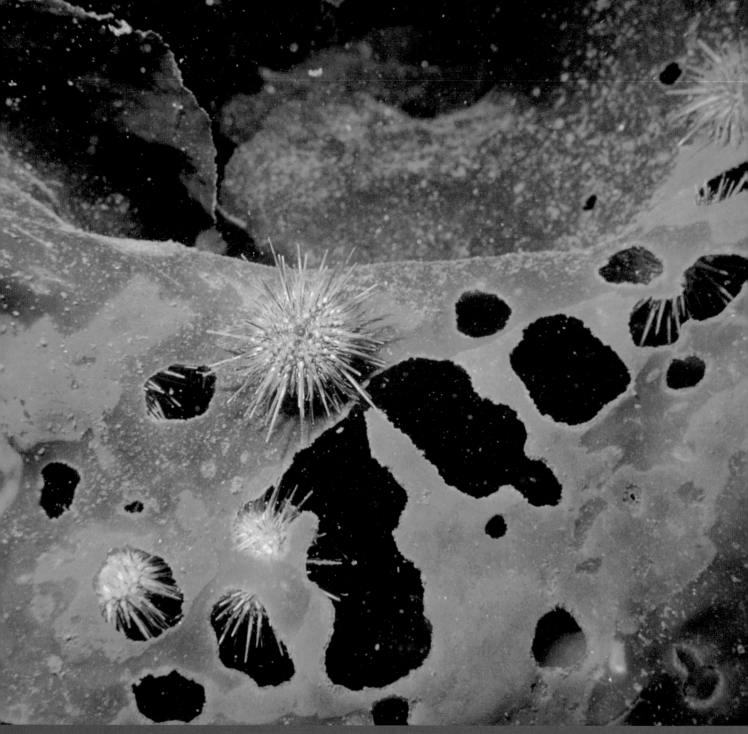

Sea urchins grazing kelp frond

Foreword

The seas around Scotland are home to an amazing and dazzling array of wildlife. Here is one of the best kept secrets of our outstanding wealth of natural heritage; it is a testament to just how well kept a secret it is that many people in Scotland probably know more about the wonders of the Great Barrier Reef or the Red Sea than of places like St Kilda and the sea lochs of the west coast. In fact, the marine wildlife of Scotland is every bit as diverse and colourful, and this booklet is a celebration of a small part of this natural and cultural heritage.

More often than not, Scotland appears encircled by a forbidding, often steely grey and stormy sea, although there are those rare, magical calm and sunny days when its surrounding seas take on an altogether more inviting hue. A look just beneath the surface can reveal a wealth of hidden treasures. Nowhere is this more so than in the great forests of kelp that are perfectly adapted to thrive in these stormy conditions, and are host to a multitude of other creatures. The stipes of the kelp are draped with other seaweeds and a wide variety of animals and the underlying rock surfaces are an explosion of colour and form with many of the animals having no counterparts on land. Within the water column of this submarine forest, fish cruise around and seals and otters hunt for prey.

A trip through these forests is a voyage of discovery, with something new to excite the senses at every turn. This booklet in the SNH series 'Scotland's Living Landscapes' presents a brief insight into the life of the kelp forests and is the latest in this series which aims to inform and engage readers in a greater appreciation of our outstanding natural heritage. For many readers it will, I believe, provide a tantalising glimpse into a seriously under-rated part of our natural world.

Jeff Watson
SNH Director with responsibility
for the marine environment.

Kelp holdfast and stipe with featherstars, brittlestars and other starfish

Introduction

A HIDDEN RESOURCE

Walk down to the seaward edge of a rocky shore in Scotland at low tide on a bright, calm day and you will see the stalks (or 'stipes') of kelp plants sticking out of the sea, brown and glistening in the gently moving water. The stipes will be bent over by the fronds (or 'blades') of the plants, themselves occasionally visible between the waves.

If the tide is low enough, and the water calm enough, you may glimpse some of the animals and plants which live on and between the kelp plants in the shallows. You will see tiny jewel-like limpets, brightly coloured anemones, spiny sea urchins, darting fish, and delicate red seaweeds.

This is the upper fringe of the vast kelp forest, a diverse community of plants and animals which extends from the lower shore down into the sea, sometimes to depths of greater than 20m and exceptionally to 40m+ and extending up to 5 km offshore where there is a gently shelving sea bed. Kelp forests are biologically rich, are relatively accessible to study, and yet many of their secrets remain undiscovered. Kelp forests occur extensively in coastal waters and not only form an important part of Scotland's natural heritage, but have also provided an important economic resource in the past, particularly in the Highlands and the Islands, and continue to do so to this day. Cast kelp, or 'tangle' is still collected for fertilising machair, and for industrial processing.

Kelp beds exposed at low tide, Lochailort, Moidart

What is kelp and where is it found?

Kelps occur at and below low-tide level in cool temperate regions throughout the world. They are a group of large brown seaweeds that live on the rocky sea bed as far down as sunlight penetration will allow. The plants often grow together in large numbers to form dense forests, usually composed of a single kelp species.

There are two major groups of kelps. The laminarian kelps of the northern hemisphere, including British coastal waters, typically have strap-like blades and a relatively short stipe. In the South Atlantic, Pacific and Indian Oceans there is a second category of kelps - the 'bladder kelps' - which have greatly elongated flexible stipes bearing gas-filled bladders near the top. The bladders serve to buoy up the plants to help them make best use of surface sunlight. Both groups of kelps are attached to the sea bed by a structure called a holdfast. The holdfast has a superficial similarity to the root system of terrestrial plants; however, it does not penetrate

Holdfasts of oarweed on rock encrusted with sponges and pink calcareous seaweed

the sea bed as the roots of land plants penetrate the soil, nor is it involved in the transfer of nutrients, which kelp plants derive directly from seawater.

The bladder kelps include the giant kelp, *Macrocystis pyrifera*, which is the largest marine plant known on earth. This plant, which forms dense beds off the coast of California, can grow up to 50m in length. Under optimal growing conditions, it can increase in length at a rate of 1m per day!

Laminarian kelp forests, composed mainly of cuvie, *Laminaria hyperborea*, are found on suitable rocky areas all around the Scottish coastline, reaching their greatest extent where the sea bed slopes gently away from the land. They are less common along the east coast, where much of the sea bed is composed of sand, and are particularly extensive around Skye and the adjacent mainland, along the west coast of the Outer Hebrides, and around Orkney and Shetland.

Cuvie

KEY:

Laminaria
Macrocystis
Ecklonia

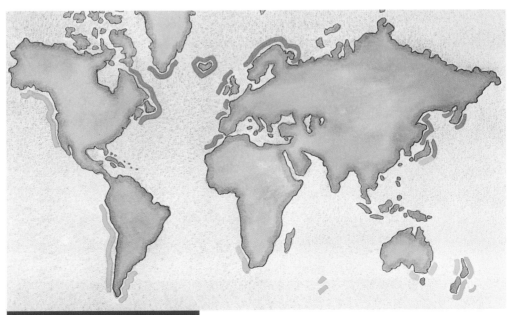

World distribution of major kelp forests (after Mann 1973)

Dense cuvie forest

Why kelp forests are important in Scottish coastal waters

Kelp stipe encrusted with sea mats

Lumpsucker on kelp with encrusting bryozoans and tubeworms

In many ways, kelp forests are the Scottish equivalent of tropical coral reefs; both are found in shallow coastal waters, and both perform similar functions in the marine environment.

Kelp forests and coral reefs provide three-dimensional 'living space' for animals and plants. Small animals such as worms and crustaceans live in gaps in the branching kelp holdfasts, while the plant surfaces support a diverse range of colonial animals (such as sea mats and sponges) and red seaweeds. Animals and plants also live on the rock surface between kelp plants, and small fish shelter from predators in the shade of the blades.

A column of water in which a giant kelp plant grows can support several thousand times as many animals as a column of water stretching above a barren ocean floor. Although an equivalent figure cannot be given for Scottish kelp plants, it is known that large numbers of animals live in the forests in comparison to areas devoid of kelp.

5

A second important function of both kelp forests and coral reefs is the production of organic material. In a similar way to land plants, kelps and the other seaweeds found in kelp forests grow by fixing carbon dioxide through the process of photosynthesis. The resulting vegetation eventually dies, producing flakes of rotting plant material and dissolved chemicals derived from plant material, both of which act as food sources for bacteria and single-celled animals. These, in turn, provide food for larger animals such as fish and lobsters. This is similar to a forest on land, where rotting leaf-litter enriches the soil and encourages the growth of mites and insects which are eaten by birds, hedgehogs and badgers.

In a coral reef, the organic material is produced by millions of tiny one-celled plants which live in association with the coral, and by a range of other seaweeds living on the reef.

Fringing reefs around coral islands protect the islands from oceanic storms, and prevent these vulnerable, low-lying outcrops of coral sand from being washed away by the waves. In a similar way, it is believed that kelp forests reduce the erosive impact of Atlantic waves on some Scottish shores, in particular those of the Outer Hebrides and Northern Isles.

Atlantic waves, North Uist

Ampiphods on kelp frond
covered with sea mat

Dabberlocks

Scottish kelp plants

Five kelp species are found around Scotland. They each have a distinctive appearance, and they can also be distinguished by the situations in which they grow, defined by depth and range of exposure to wave action.

Oarweed, *Laminaria digitata*, is the kelp most likely to be seen by the casual observer. It grows at low-tide level on most open coast rocky shores, where it forms the upper fringe of the kelp forest. It can also be found in lower shore rock pools. It has a flexible smooth stipe and a leathery blade, divided into thin straps which spread out like the fingers of a hand. It is tough in texture but smooth to the touch, and lies nearly flat on the shore when the tide is out. It is designed to move with the waves as they crash on the shore; its flexibility allows it to live and grow in situations where a more rigid plant would be torn off the rock.

Dabberlocks
Alaria esculenta

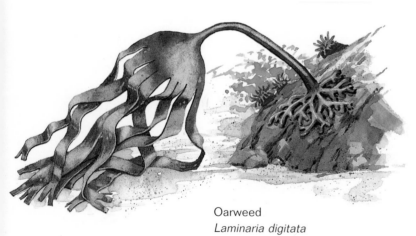

Oarweed
Laminaria digitata

On Scottish shores which are subject to severe wave action, such as west-facing shores open to the full force of Atlantic storms, even oarweed cannot survive and is replaced by dabberlocks, *Alaria esculenta*, as the dominant kelp at low-tide level. Dabberlocks is a long, pointed, narrow plant with a short stipe; it is even more flexible than oarweed, and has a thinner frond with a distinctive midrib. On many shores, however, oarweed and dabberlocks are found together, with dabberlocks on wave-exposed headlands and at cliff bases, particularly where these are steeply sloping, and oarweed in more sheltered areas. The fronds of dabberlocks are often eroded by the savage battering they take from storms.

Large, individual plants of cuvie, *Laminaria hyperborea*, are occasionally visible in some oarweed forests. Cuvie is similar in appearance to oarweed, but can be distinguished by its large size and rough, stiff stipe which stands upright at low tide and is often covered by a profusion of attached red seaweed. Below the oarweed forest, and out of the immediate reach of the waves, cuvie is the most abundant kelp species, and is the dominant component of the extensive kelp forests which surround much of the open coast of Scotland.

Sugar kelp
Laminaria saccharina

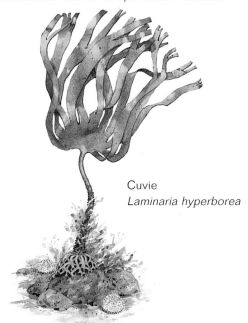

Cuvie
Laminaria hyperborea

Furbellows, *Saccorhiza polyschides*, is less common than other Scottish kelp species, but may be locally abundant. It is found at and below extreme low water, and is more common on sheltered shores than on the open coast. The blade is similar to that of oarweed and cuvie but the plant is distinguished by its frilled stipe and bulbous, warty holdfast, which is hollow and often provides a home for small fish and other animals.

Sugar kelp, *Laminaria saccharina*, is an opportunist species which can sometimes occur on exposed shores, but which is most commonly encountered in areas sheltered from wave action, such as bays or the inner reaches of many sea lochs. Sugar kelp has a short stipe and a long, wavy, undivided frond without a midrib. It is found from low-tide level to the limit of available light. In the most sheltered areas, it adopts a 'cape form', characterised by a wide, shapeless wavy frond, sometimes larger than a bath towel, which is attached to the sea bed by a small, weak holdfast.

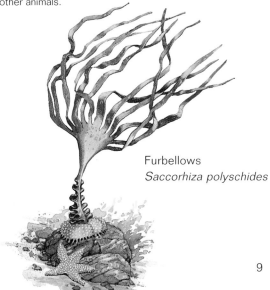

Furbellows
Saccorhiza polyschides

9

Light - the critical factor

Light is absorbed by seawater; the deeper you are in the sea, the darker it becomes. Kelp and all other seaweeds only occur in relatively shallow areas of the sea, where light intensity is high enough to permit photosynthesis. This layer is known as the photic zone. Within this zone there is a critical depth, different for each species of seaweed, above which the particular species can obtain sufficient light energy for growth and reproduction, but below which this is not possible.

However, the densest kelp growth does not take place at light levels approaching those of critical depth, but in shallower water where light intensity is higher. Cuvie forests typically extend to a depth of about 20m off the west coast such as the Outer Hebrides, and to only about 10m off north-east Scotland.

10

Sugar kelp

Individual, scattered kelp plants can survive down to the depth at which average light values fall to 1% of that at the surface. Some smaller red seaweeds require even less light and therefore have a greater critical depth. In clean, clear, west coast sea water kelp is found down to depths of 30m, and in the crystal clear waters around St Kilda it has been recorded at 47m. In the more turbid waters of north-east Scotland, however, it grows only down to between 18m and 20m and in many places much shallower than this such as in the peaty waters of many of the sea lochs.

On the open coast the density of the kelp declines with depth as the light intensity decreases. The term 'forest' is used to refer to the dense stands of kelp that are found in shallower water, subject to higher ambient light intensity. In this region only a limited amount of light can penetrate through the massed kelp fronds (or 'canopy') to the sea bed. The kelp 'park' occurs at greater depths; plants are more widely scattered than in the 'forest', allowing more of the ambient light to penetrate to the sea bed. The boundary between the 'forest' and the 'park' can be as a shallow as 4m in turbid areas, and in clear water at anything from 14m to 30m.

Oarweed forests

Sea slug

Butterfish, fanworm, red seaweeds, seasquirts and sea mats on kelp stipe

The oarweed forest marks the junction between land and sea. It is probably one of the most 'natural' environments that can be explored by a land dweller, in that, around most of Scotland, it is only rarely affected by human activity. A close look at the world beneath the oarweed blades at low tide reveals a wonderland of delicately textured seaweeds and peculiar creatures, many of which have no counterpart on land.

Walking across the oarweed forest with the tide at its lowest means moving over a slippery, tangled brown mass of kelp blades, with clumps of other seaweed, such as crisp purple carragheen, *Mastocarpus stellatus*, dotted here and there on the rock. The rock surface itself is splashed in places with flashes of vivid pink. On closer examination, these are seen to be thin, chalky encrustations layered on top of the rock. These seemingly inert patches are in fact red seaweeds, which capture dissolved minerals from sea water to form their own chalky deposits.

Greyish-white encrustations can be seen on many of the kelp blades. These are bryozoans or moss-animals, also known as sea mats. Dull, irregular patches to the naked eye, they appear as regularly patterned mosaics under the microscope, each tile of the mosaic a small chamber containing a tiny animal. Superficially similar are the hydroids or sea-firs (once termed 'zoophytes' because they were considered part animal and part plant), which form small branching erect colonies. These have an outer supporting skeleton of horny material, interrupted by openings through which project the microscopic tentacled feeding heads or 'polyps' of the living animals.

Edible crab and sea anemones

Sea slugs grazing sea mats on kelp frond

Bloody Henry starfish

Dahlia anemone

Also present on the kelp blades is the translucent blue-rayed limpet, *Helcion pellucidum*, with its characteristic lines of vivid blue spots, reminiscent in their intensity of the colours of tropical fish. This limpet migrates down to the oarweed holdfast when it grows older; its shell becomes thicker and the colours fade.

Blue-rayed limpet

A wide variety of animals live in the small chambers formed between the branching, root-like holdfast. These include fast-moving carnivorous bristle worms, with hooked, pincer-like black jaws, slow-moving scale-worms, and small, tube-dwelling crustaceans. Tiny, five-armed brittle stars and small crabs may also be seen.

Other animals attach to the rock surface between kelp plants and under boulders. Sponges form splurges of colour or tubular vase or purse shapes under overhanging rocks. Flower-like sea anemones are among the most strikingly coloured and patterned creatures of the shore, and orange or white soft corals, composed of many small polyps contained in a tough, rubbery mass, adorn the kelp stipes and rock surfaces in the shallow sublittoral.

Colonial sea squirts grow as thin sheets over rocks and seaweeds; many minute, brightly coloured individuals are arranged in double rows or starry patterns within a jelly-like matrix. Solitary sea squirts are bag-like animals, up to 7cm or 8cm high; two small openings squirt out water in fine jets when the animal is pressed.

Other animals of the oarweed forest live unattached to the rock surface or kelp plants. Close examination of clumps of seaweed may reveal grotesquely armoured sea spiders that feed on hydroids and sea anemones, tearing them apart with hooked pincers. A flash of bright purple or yellow may reveal the presence of a sea slug. Despite their name, these shell-less molluscs are among the most beautiful of marine animals, delicate in form and vividly coloured, although they are often very small.

Starfish glide slowly over the boulders between kelp plants, and an occasional sea urchin can be seen sheltering from the sun in the shade of an oarweed blade. A turned-over boulder may reveal a fast-moving blue and red squat-lobster, or an edible crab with 'pie crust' markings. When wading through shallow pools or peering under boulders you may disturb a butterfish, and glimpse its brown and black marbled back as it twists its eel-like body. You may also see the spiky-finned shanny, and the rounded, tadpole-like sea snail, which clings to the underside of rocks by means of a sucker.

The rock surface beneath the kelp park covered with encrusting animals and red seaweeds in a kaleidoscope of colour

Cuvie forests

At around 1m below low-water level, oarweed gives way to cuvie in all but the most sheltered areas, forming an extensive seaweed habitat around much of the British Isles. This forest is never uncovered by the tide. Kelp fronds drift back and forth in slow synchrony, moved by the pulse of the waves. From above, the sea floor is invisible beneath a wide band of gently swaying fronds.

From within the kelp forest, on all but the calmest days, the 2-3m high plants form a moving curtain, shading the sea bed but allowing occasional shafts of sunlight to penetrate the gloom. Beneath the canopy of large plants the growth of younger plants is restricted by the lack of light and the smaller plants form a distinct sub-layer under the waving fronds. These cannot reach their full height unless a storm or other event tears a hole in the canopy and allows light to flood in.

Other seaweeds grow on the kelp stipes, like lichens on tree trunks. The stipes are swathed in a pink veil of membranous and filamentous red seaweed, including the ribbon-like *Membranoptera alata*, sea oak, *Phycodrys rubens*, dark red *Palmaria palmata* and feathery *Ptilota plumosa*. Animals also settle on the rough, erect stipes of cuvie including brightly coloured sea squirts, sponges and tufts of hydroids and erect bryozoans, feather stars and soft corals.

The large, dome-shaped cuvie holdfasts contain many tiny chambers, each chamber a grotto with its resident speck of animal life. These might include five-armed brittle stars, tiny tiger-striped amphipods with huge claws in relation to their size, delicate sedentary worms which extend a fine tracery of feeding tentacles into the water, and colourful sea slugs and sponges. The holdfasts also trap sediment, which provides a food source for some of their miniscule inhabitants.

The sea bed between the holdfasts is often covered by a living turf of both animals and plants. Grey-white tufts or branching fronds of erect sea firs and sea mats are common within this turf, each composed of hundreds or thousands of individual animals, arranged together in a stiff, plant-like colony. There are also larger attached animals, such as sponges, anemones and the rubbery, flesh-coloured soft coral, dead man's fingers *Alcyonium digitatum*.

As a diver you could part this turf with your fingers and reveal grazing animals on the rock surface, including chitons or coat-of-mail shells, and other molluscs. Shrimps and small fish such as scorpion fish, blennies and gobies would dart away from your hands. You might also see some of the larger denizens of the forest, including the colourful Ballan wrasse, sea urchins and, if you're lucky, the feelers of a lobster protruding from a crevice in the sea bed.

In some areas of reduced exposure to wave action, grazing by sea urchins and various molluscs can be intense, resulting in bare rock between the holdfasts, and kelp stipes devoid of seaweed.

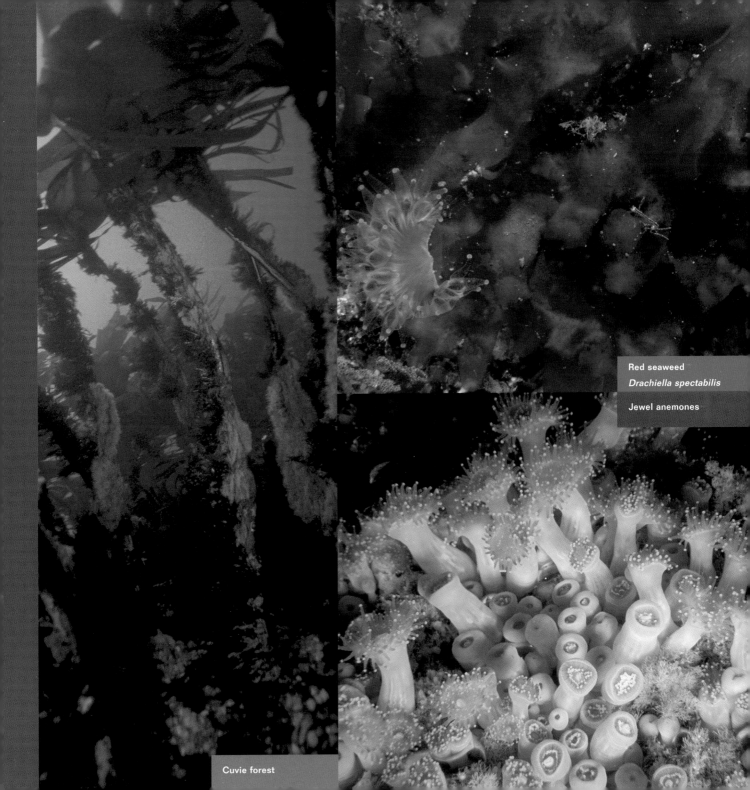

Red seaweed
Drachiella spectabilis

Jewel anemones

Cuvie forest

Kelp parks

Kelp parks support an extraordinary variety of animals and seaweeds, with a wide range of species and growth forms. The absence of a dense, shading canopy of kelp fronds permits the development of lush meadows of waving red seaweeds including sea beech, *Delesseria sanguinea,* and *Hypoglossum hypoglossoides.* This algal carpet provides a living substrate for encrusting sea mats, and for small crustaceans, worms and molluscs.

The number of animal species in the kelp park is, if anything, greater than the number in the kelp forest, especially on the rock surface. In some shaded areas several square metres of bedrock may be covered by single species or mixed associations of sea anemones, sea squirts, sponges or erect sea mats and sea firs. In other areas the tortuously twisted limy tubes made by the keel worm, *Pomatoceros triqueter,* may cover the sea bed. The solitary Devonshire cup-coral, *Caryophyllia smithii,* is also frequently found.

Mobile animals of the kelp park (which may also be found in the forest above) include the spiny starfish, *Marthasterias glacialis,* which can grow up to 60cm across, the spectacular 10 or 12-armed common sunstar, *Crossaster papposus,* and several crab species such as the spider crab, *Hyas araneus.* The feather star, *Antedon bifida,* congregates on vertical rock surfaces and the kelp stipes.

In areas the kelp park, like the kelp forest, is heavily grazed, and the variety of associated animals and seaweeds is much reduced. The only animals visible on the sea bed are grazers, particularly sea urchins and molluscs, with occasional patches of brittlestars. The luxuriant seaweed growth of the ungrazed kelp park is replaced by thin, encrusting films which look like stains on the seabed.

Descending deeper into the sea, the motion of the kelp plants becomes more gentle and the noise of breaking waves near the surface recedes. It also becomes darker, as sea water absorbs more and more of the surface light. The kelp forest grades imperceptibly into kelp park. Here the kelp plants are more widely scattered, and individual plants are smaller, with shorter stipes and thinner blades.

Velvet crab and featherstars underneath kelp

Starfish and sea anemones

Sunstar, sponges and dead man's fingers

Beyond the kelp zone

In the dark, quiet areas below the kelp zone, plant domination of the sea bed gives way to animal domination. Several species of small red seaweeds and encrusting seaweeds can grow at greater depths than kelp, but even these eventually succumb to the decreasing light levels. However, the flick of a diver's torch reveals an unsuspected world of dazzling colours and strange growth forms. Delicate, feathery hydroids and sea fans and elegant fan worms grow among large erect sponges and sea squirts which attain sizes rarely seen in shallower water. Dense colonies of the brilliantly coloured jewel anemone form bright green and red patches on vertical surfaces, interspersed with the waving arms of feather stars. Many animals which are familiar from shallower waters also live at these depths, including starfish, brittle stars, sea urchins and dead man's fingers.

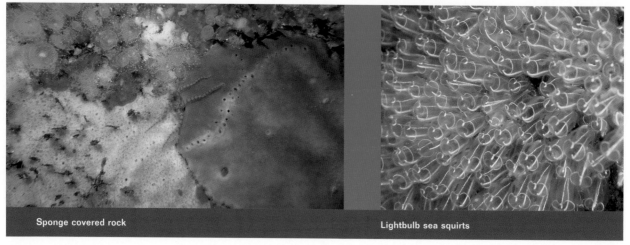

Sponge covered rock

Lightbulb sea squirts

Mammals and birds

Otter in oarweed forest at low tide

Otters are scarce throughout much of Europe, and Scotland is one of the few countries with a thriving population.

Some of the healthiest remaining Scottish otter populations inhabit the coastal areas of Orkney, Shetland, the Western Isles and the western Highlands. These animals rarely travel more than 50m off shore, and forage for food on the sea bed in 3-10m depth of water, where they catch crabs and small fish such as butterfish and sea scorpions. Although they also forage on intertidal seaweed beds, particularly in sea lochs, kelp forests are an important habitat on the open coast. The animals prefer forests with open areas or holes, where they can hunt without being hampered by the kelp.

Little is known about the use of kelp forests by sea birds, although it is believed that many species which feed in open water, such as gannets, would be discouraged by the tightly packed kelp stipes and fronds, which reduce their underwater manoeuvrability. However some seabirds, for example, black guillemots or 'tysties' almost certainly use gaps in the forest and the more open kelp park for hunting small fish and crabs.

Even when dead, cast kelp provides an invaluable habitat for certain waders such as turnstones and purple sandpipers, which hunt for small crustaceans and insect larvae hatched in the stinking soup of decaying weed.

Redshanks on the tangle

Seals above the kelp forest canopy at St Kilda

Kelp productivity

After kelp forests have been hit by winter storms, the adjacent shore is covered by a brown carpet of glistening plants that have been ripped off the sea bed by the force of the waves. All this material eventually rots and enters the marine food web.

Kelps contribute organic material to the food web in other ways. Waves continually erode the tips of kelp blades, releasing flakes of plant matter. Every spring each cuvie plant sheds its blade from the previous year; an enormous input of detritus into the marine ecosystem, when the size of kelp forests is taken into account. In addition to the huge volume of rotting foliage produced by kelp forests, individual plants secrete as much as 40% of their net organic production directly into the sea. The productivity of kelp forests has been compared to the level of productivity found in a wheat field on land.

This huge amount of organic material is utilised by the animals of the kelp forest and, due to the action of waves and currents, by animals in other parts of the sea. Some animals, such as urchins, graze directly on kelp fragments. Bacteria absorb dissolved organic matter and in turn are eaten by filter-feeding invertebrates. Single-celled animals, small crustaceans, worms and molluscs trap minute particles of detritus. These, in turn, fall prey to larger animals such as fish and starfish.

The production of organic matter by kelp plants provides much of the fuel that drives the machinery of the inshore food web. Without the food source provided by kelp detritus and dissolved organic matter, inshore coastal waters would contain far fewer animals.

Mounds of cast kelp (tangle) on a sandy shore on Sanday, Orkney

Lumpsucker amongst cuvie stipes festooned in red seaweeds

Uses of kelp

Cast kelp or 'tangle' has been utilised by generations of Scots industrialists, farmers and crofters for manufacturing and agricultural purposes, especially in the Highlands and Islands.

The very name 'kelp' was first coined to mean the ash produced after tangle burning, and only later came to refer to the seaweed itself. This ash was first produced on a large scale, particularly in Orkney and the Western Isles, in the early 18th century; its high potash and soda content were used in glass and soap manufacture. At its peak, between 1780 and 1830, the industry employed several thousand people. The bulk of the ash was exported south for further processing. With the discovery of other sources of potash and soda, the industry declined.

Collected tangle set out to dry, Birsay, Orkney

It revived on a smaller scale, however, with the discovery in the 19th century that iodine could be extracted from laminarian ash, a practice which continued until the 1930s. At that time imports of cheaper iodine extracted from Chilean nitrate deposits ended the Scottish kelp industry.

Burning kelp, Birsay, Orkney (1880s)

In recent times several thousand tonnes of dried tangle have been collected each year by crofters in the Western Isles and Orkney. Cast kelp stipes are gathered from the foreshore, particularly after the wild Atlantic storms which affect the island groups, and are stacked on huge drying racks until ready for transportation to the mainland. In addition, the egg wrack, *Ascophyllum nodosum,* has been harvested from the shore. Seaweed collectors work on a self-employed basis, and the pattern of work fits in well with traditional crofting activity. These seaweeds are used, not for iodine or potash production but for the extraction of 'alginates'.

Alginates are chemicals with a wide range of applications in the food, textile, pharmaceutical and other industries. These uses depend on their gelling and emulsifying properties. The chemicals are found in products as diverse as tomato ketchup, postage stamps, medical dressings and beer (alginates are added to aid head retention). World-wide, over 0.5 million tonnes of seaweed per year is used in alginate production, much of it giant kelp, *Macrocystis pyrifera*, from California or cuvie, *Laminaria hyperborea*, from Norwegian coastal waters.

Storm-cast kelp is also collected by farmers and crofters for fertilising the soil. In the Western Isles it is ploughed into the relatively nutrient-poor sandy soils of the machair, enhancing the growth of arable crops.

Kelp harvesting

Large-scale cuvie harvesting (over 150,000 tonnes per year) takes place in Norwegian coastal waters, where it is undertaken by tug-sized custom-built vessels with open holds the size of large caravans. Kelp harvesting is managed on a rotational basis, ensuring that each area is harvested only once every 4 years to allow regrowth of the plants.

The kelp dredge itself resembles a huge, iron garden rake, 3m wide and with elongated spiked teeth, which is carried along the sea bed on raised skis. The weight of the dredge as it is pulled forward rips dozens of kelp plants from the rock, holdfast and all, which are then caught between the teeth. At the end of a harvesting run, the dredge may have been drawn 50-250m along the sea bed, and have over a tonne of plants hanging in a compact mass from its teeth.

Kelp harvesting also occurs in other areas of the world. Different harvesting methods are used for different kelp species. For example, in California the giant kelp is the basis of a huge alginate extraction industry. However, in this case only the tips of the 30m plus plants are harvested, by being cropped at the surface of the sea. The bulk of the plant remains attached to the seabed after harvesting, in contrast to cuvie harvesting, and the fast growth rate ensures rapid replacement of harvestable plant material.

Kelp harvesting has been considered in Scottish waters, using Norwegian-style kelp dredges, and pilot studies have been carried out. Freshly harvested weed provides higher quality raw material for alginate production than tangle, due

Diver framed between the stipes of two furbellow plants

to differing amounts of decay in the latter before drying. Harvested material is also more readily accessible, and available in larger volumes, than tangle from the isles.

There are a number of important factors which should be addressed in the management of any harvesting operation should it happen in the future. For example, in Norway the 4-year reharvesting period results in growth of smaller plants with fewer associated animals and seaweed than a mature kelp forest. This means that the kelp has fewer contaminants to remove prior to alginate processing, but also that the forest itself is impoverished in comparison to

Crabs inside creel in kelp

an unharvested forest. A 6 or 7 year reharvesting cycle has recently been suggested in Norway, not only to allow better development of the kelp-dependant communities, but also to fit in with natural cycles of population changes in kelps.

Other factors which may have a bearing on management of kelp harvesting activity include the role of urchin grazing in recovery of the kelp forest after harvesting, and the importance of kelp forests as a habitat for lobsters and pelagic fish species.

Anecdotal evidence from Norway and California links kelp removal with coastal erosion. Kelp forests may play a part in reducing coastal erosion by damping down the force of incoming waves before they hit the shore, and by reducing current-induced sand movement around their holdfasts. Although this is only speculation at present, this factor may require further investigation before large-scale kelp removal takes place at potentially vulnerable sites around Scotland.

Afterword

The brown, sunlight-dappled fronds of a kelp forest swaying gently on the shallow sea bed hide a complex, interconnecting web of life which is as yet poorly understood. The lives and deaths of plants in the forest provide food for numerous invertebrate animals and fish. The importance of this organic material probably extends far beyond the immediate vicinity of the forest itself. In addition, storm-cast kelp plants have presented a sea gift of fertiliser and raw materials to Scottish coastal communities for generations.

If more direct human exploitation of the forest is to be carried out, then this should be managed on the basis of a sound scientific knowledge of the kelp forest ecosystem, and a respect for its creatures, so that the forests can continue to play their role as an important aspect of Scotland's marine natural heritage.

Further Reading

Barnes, R.S.K., and Hughes, R.N. 1988, *An Introduction to Marine Ecology*. Blackwell Scientific Publications, Oxford

Baxter, J.M., and Usher, M.B. (eds) 1994. *The Islands of Scotland: A Living Marine Heritage*. HMSO, Edinburgh.

Fish J.D., and Fish, S. 1989. *A Student's Guide to the Seashore*. Unwin Hyman, London.

Guiry, M.D., and Blunden, G (eds) 1991. *Seaweed Resources in Europe:* Uses and Potential. John Wiley & Sons, London.

McPeak, R.H., Glantz, D.A., and Shaw, C.R. *The Amber Forest. Beauty and Biology of California's Submarine Forests*.

Thomson, W.P.L. 1983. Kelp Making in Orkney. The Orkney Press, Kirkwall.

Wilkinson, M. 1995. *Information Review on the Impact of Kelp Harvesting*. Scottish Natural Heritage Review No. 34. Scottish Natural Heritage, Edinburgh.

Wood, E.M. 1987. *Subtidal Ecology*. Edward Arnold, London.

28

Ballan wrasse in kelp forest

Also in Scotland's Living Landscapes series

If you have enjoyed Kelp Forests why not find out more about Scotland's distinctive habitats in our Scotland's Living Landscapes series. Each 'landscape' is a dynamic environment supporting a wealth of plants and animals, whose lives are woven inextricably together. The colourfully illustrated booklets explore these complex relationships simply and concisely, and explain why they are important and what needs to be done to protect them for the future.

Sea Lochs

Featuring dramatic underwater photography, this booklet tells why Scotland's sea lochs are so special to people living around their shores and to the magnificent wildlife that depends on their sheltered waters.

Sue Scott
ISBN 1 85397 246 0 pbk 24pp £3.00

Firths

Firths lie at the heart of Scottish life: they support our economy, house most of our population, and provide a precious home for wildlife. Discover the magic of our unsung firths and the efforts being made to secure their future.

Steve Atkins
ISBN 1 85397 271 1 pbk 36pp £3.50

Machair

Machair is a rare coastal habitat widely recognised for its swathes of colourful wildflowers and abundant bird life. Find out how machair resulted from natural forces combined with centuries of careful land management.

John Love
ISBN 1 85397 001 8 pbk 28pp £3.00

Coasts

Scotland has nearly 12,000km of coastline, much of it remote, unspoilt and strikingly beautiful. Learn all about this changing environment, the unique habitats, landforms and wildlife and the many pressures they face.

George Lees & Kathy Duncan
ISBN 1 85397 003 4 pbk 28pp £3.00

Boglands

Bogland is one of Britain's most undervalued habitats. This booklet challenges the conventional view of boglands and rewards its reader with vivid images of the colourful and intriguing wildlife of bogs.

Richard Lindsay
ISBN 1 85397 120 2 pbk 20pp £2.00

Soils

As all gardeners know, what grows on the surface depends on what's beneath their feet. Indeed soils are home to a all sorts of animals as well as plants. This booklet relates the story of our soils to the landscapes we see everyday.

Andrew Taylor & Stephen Nortcliff
ISBN 1 85397 223 1 pbk 24pp £2.50

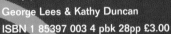

Landscape Fashioned by Geology series

The Landscape Fashioned by Geology series helps you to explore the rocks that lie beneath the soils, trees and heather with clear explanations, stunning photographs and illustrations. Produced in collaboration with the British Geological Survey, each booklet is written by experts in a style which is accessible to all.

Scotland: The Creation of its Natural Landscape
Alan McKirdy and Roger Crofts
ISBN 1 85397 004 2 pbk 64pp £7.50

Skye
David Stephenson & Jon Merritt
ISBN 1 85397 026 3 pbk 24pp £2.50

Cairngorms
John Gordon, Vanessa Brazier & Sarah Keast
ISBN 1 85397 086 7 pbk 28pp £2.00

Edinburgh
David McAdam
ISBN 1 85397 024 7 pbk 28pp £2.50

Orkney and Shetland
Clive Auton, Terry Fletcher & David Gould
ISBN 1 85397 220 7 pbk 24pp £2.50

East Lothian and the Borders
David McAdam & Phil Stone
ISBN 1 85397 242 8 pbk 26pp £3.00

Loch Lomond to Stirling
Mike Browne & J.R.Mendum
ISBN 1 85397 119 7 pbk 26pp £2.00

Arran and the Clyde Islands
David McAdam & Steve Robertson
ISBN 1 85397 287 8 pbk 24pp £3.00

Naturally Scottish series

Scotland has more than 65,000 species of plants and animals. The Naturally Scottish series looks at the different aspects of Scotland's rich natural heritage. Each book is illustrated with exceptional photographs by top wildlife photographers that not only show the species, but illustrate their habitats and their relationship with man. They also provide helpful information on conservation and the law.

Red Squirrels
Peter Lurz & Mairi Cooper
ISBN 1 85397 298 4 pbk 20pp £3.00

Burnet Moths
Mark Young
ISBN 1 85397 209 6 pbk 24pp £3.00

Sea Eagles
Greg Mudge, Kevin Duffy, Kate Thompson & John Love
ISBN 1 85397 208 8 pbk 16pp £1.50

Badgers
Mairi Cooper & John Ralston
ISBN 1 85397 254 1 pbk 16pp £3.00

Seals
Elizabeth Cruwys and John Baxter
ISBN 1 85397 233 9 pbk 24pp £3.00

Whales, Dolphins & Porpoises
Sandy Kerr (ed.)
ISBN 1 85397 210 X pbk 24pp £3.00

(all prices may be subject to change)